THE AUCHENHARVIE COLLIERY
an early history

Compiled by the Three Towns Local History Group

contributors:

Alec Phillips, Kenneth Luckhurst, William Gray,
Thomas McLean, Neil Johnson, Isa McMaster,
Ambrose Taylor, Kenneth Jackson
Jean Symington Richmond and Alice Wilson

project co-ordinator and author

Irene Hughson

FOREWORD

The material for this publication has been researched by the Three Towns Local History Group, a flourishing offshoot of the W.E.A.'s Living with Leisure Group which meets in Ardrossan. The Local History Group has published two previous titles - *Ardrossan Shipyards: The Struggle for Survival (1825-1983)* and *Ardrossan Harbour (1805-1970)*. It was during their search for information about the harbour that members of the Group first made use of the Auchenharvie Papers, and realised that they represented a very valuable historical resource indeed.

The Auchenharvie Papers are estate papers belonging to the Cunninghame family, one of whose members pioneered coal working in North Ayrshire. They were found in a large hamper in the attic of Seabank House, once the Cunninghame family home, when it came into the possession of Mr. Kirkland, a lawyer in Saltcoats. He presented them to Saltcoats Town Council who put them into the care of Saltcoats Museum Society. During the 1950s Owen Kelly, a founder member and the driving force behind the Society, took on the formidable task of going through and cataloguing several hundred individual items, some written in Latin on parchment, others in beautiful but faded copperplate script on paper. Notes on an informal talk given by Mr. Kelly in October 1956 describe how he and a small group of volunteers, christened the 'Auchenharvie Brotherhood', began sorting out the damp and dusty papers:

> The first thing I had to do was to get them ironed out in order
> to be thoroughly dried and, where necessary, rubbed with
> breadcrumbs to take off the dust and dirt of ages. Many
> of them had to be repaired with gum paper. To show the
> labour connected with this work, I may mention that one long
> roll, over 20 feet in length, took over five hours to clean and
> repair.

The papers were then grouped according to subject and filed in pigeon holes in tin trunks donated for the purpose. Mr. Kelly expressed the hope that in the future "we shall have local enthusiasts who will select the subject that pleases them and write brochures or short histories".

Forty years later the group has done just that, for the most part relying on photocopies of the originals housed in the Local History Section of Ardrossan Library, but on occasions, when the text was particularly obscure, going back to the original to seek clarification. Most of the papers are personal letters and memoranda, and many of them are undated. It was only after long and patient study that the complicated story of the Cunninghames and their involvement in coal production and exportation began to be pieced together.

While the Auchenharvie Papers have proved to be the Group's main source of information for this project, other sources have been useful in providing corroborating evidence.[1] We have had some recourse to the Warner Papers, another amorphous collection of family documents held by the Scottish Record Office, and to the Lowther Papers held in Carlisle Record Office. The huge deposit of material (numbering over a thousand hand-written pages) relating to the long drawn out court cases between Warner and Cunninghame contained in the Scottish Record Office was consulted on several occasions. Fortunately, a collection of abstracts concerning the court cases was available closer to home in the Local History Section of Ardrossan Library.

Many other sources have been consulted and references are made to them in the text. Of particular value in helping us to set what happened at Auchenharvie within the local context was Dr C. Whatley's unpublished thesis *The Process of Industrialisation in Ayrshire c1707-1871* which can be consulted in the Carnegie Library in Ayr and the same writer's monograph in the Ayrshire Collections, *The Finest Place for a Lasting Colliery*. B. C. Duckham's *History of the Scottish Coal Industry 1700-1815* helped us to set Auchenharvie within the pattern of development nationally.

[1] All information and quoted text comes from the Auchenharvie Papers unless otherwise stated.

INTRODUCTION

The three towns of Stevenston, Saltcoats, and Ardrossan stand shoulder to shoulder in the Cunninghame district of Ayrshire, at no great distance from the historic Burghs of Kilwinning and Irvine. Recently, they have been undergoing a process of renewal following the near collapse, with associated consequences in human hardship and environmental dereliction, of the industries which sustained them, and indeed, brought them into being in the first place.

There is ample evidence, going back a thousand years, of settlement, agriculture and other economic activity in the surrounding countryside, and the ruins of Kerelaw and Ardrossan Castles bear witness to the strategic importance these coastal sites had in the Middle Ages. But the linked histories of the three towns really begin to unfold with the development of industrialisation - coal was the resource on which the three towns' fortunes depended.

The Ayrshire Coalfield is an extensive one and Stevenston and Saltcoats lie on its north-western edge. The presence of coal in this area was known for a long time, although the resource was only worked casually according to demand - for instance after a wet summer when it had been difficult to cut and dry sufficient quantities of peat to last through winter. As there were seams near the surface, coal could be got out of shallow coal heuchs without the necessity of sinking shafts. Estate tenants and workers turned their hands to digging coal as and when needed and, in the village of Saltcoats, coal was regularly used for small-scale salt-making.

For the large scale commercial exploitation of any resource to be successful, the existence of the resource itself is not enough; there has to be a market for it. However, in contrast to the situation in Fife and the Lothians, there was little demand for coal in the south-west of Scotland before the 18th century. It was not favoured as a domestic fuel because of the smoke and fumes that it produced; a serious problem when the hearths in many ordinary country people's houses were centrally placed. Peat, which burned with very little smoke, made a fire that was more suitable to cook over, and the better off could command supplies of timber to burn in their broad-chimneyed fireplaces. The only demand for coal came from blacksmiths who needed either coal or charcoal to burn at high temperature in their forges. Charcoal was also in great demand for smelting ores; the sulphur content in coal made it unsuitable for the metallurgical processes in use at the time.

It was really only when peat, timber, or charcoal were temporarily unavailable that people turned to coal, and among the Eglinton Estate papers are letters from groups of tenants requesting the Earl to allow coal to be dug because of local crises in fuel supply. These requests were not always heeded. Agricultural workers could not always pay enough for coal to make it worthwhile for the Earl to arrange for its extraction.

However, as the 17th century came to a close, it became clear that local supplies of peat and timber were not going to last forever. Additionally, there was a growing demand for coal from the developing towns on Ireland's east coast whose dwindling reserves of peat and timber had to be supplemented by imported fuel. Much of Ireland's coal requirement was already being met by coal masters in the north-west of England, but there were those who saw the opportunities for commercial gain in Ayrshire. Not least among these was Robert Cunninghame[1] of Auchenharvie.

[1] The name of Cunninghame is spelt in various ways in the Auchenharvie Papers and in other sources. For consistency we have decided to stick to one spelling, and opted for 'Cunninghame' as it appears to be the most frequently used.

THE CUNNINGHAMES OF AUCHENHARVIE

Auchenharvie was part of the coal-rich lands of the Barony of Stevenston, which originally belonged to the Cunninghames of Glencairn. After passing into the hands of two other families, the Barony was bought back by Sir Robert Cunninghame, from the then Earl of Eglinton in 1656. A scion of the Glencairn family, he was appointed Physician to Charles II shortly after his coronation at Scone on 1st January 1651 and was in the King's entourage in September of that year when the royal army was defeated at Worcester. Sir Robert was taken prisoner and spent some time in the Tower of London before he was ransomed. Although his royal patron was in exile, Sir Robert's skills were much in demand and he became prosperous enough to buy the Barony.[1]

During Sir Robert's lifetime, the income from the Barony was derived almost entirely from agriculture, although some revenue was generated by salt panning, which was carried out near Saltcoats. According to the Rev. Mr Wodrow, minister of Stevenston Parish a century later, "it [salt] was then made by poor people in their little pans or kettles. They digged the coal near the surface of the ground at a very small expense and lived in huts on the shore."[2]

After his death in 1676, Sir Robert was succeeded in the Barony by his son, who only outlived his father by two years and had no children. Sir Robert's daughter could not inherit the estate when her brother died because it was entailed, and instead the land passed through the male line to her cousin, Robert Cunninghame. Robert Cunninghame of Auchenharvie came into possession of the Barony in 1678.

[1] Robertson, G: *A Genealogical Account of The Principal Families in Ayrshire, Vol. 1*
[2] *Old Statistical Account*

A VERY ENTERPRISING GENIUS

It was Robert Cunninghame of Auchenharvie who initiated the first large-scale developments in the Stevenston coalfield. To begin with he set about "prooving the coals"[1], that is, commissioning a survey in an attempt to establish the extent of the deposits, their exact location, the number, thickness and declivity of the seams, as well as the sort of difficulties that would need to be overcome in order to extract the coal.

Although this may sound like an obvious first step, it was one that was rarely taken in Cunninghame's day, being an expensive undertaking which meant laying out capital for no immediate financial return. A survey was probably deemed particularly unnecessary when surface outcrops could be readily seen, as was the case with the Ayrshire coalfield. Most proprietors were content to work these seams in piece-meal fashion.

Sir John Clerk of Penicuik, a contemporary of Cunninghame's, whose family had for many years been involved in exploiting parts of the Lothian coalfield, advised landowners with an interest in developing coal working on their land to examine hillsides "after great rains" when there was a chance of the top-soil having been washed down to reveal hidden outcrops. He also advocated a close study of springs and water courses. If the water tasted of rusty iron, or had traces of yellowish or ochre coloured deposits in the silt, then there was a possibility that it had come from a coal seam. Another approach was to dig shallow exploratory trenches on likely ground.[2]

But Robert Cunninghame set about things in a more systematic manner than this, ordering test bores to be drilled at several locations - even though boring at that time was an expensive, time-consuming and not always a very satisfactory or reliable method of exploration.

No records of the results of the survey have survived, although it must have revealed that there was sufficient coal present to make investment in its extraction an attractive prospect. However, in addition to this, Cunninghame needed to be sure of finding an adequate amount of suitable quality coal. That meant bringing out fuel which had good burning properties and which was hard enough to withstand transportation without breaking up into dross and small pieces. Poorer quality coal, known as 'panwood', could be used in the local saltpans which were on Cunninghame's land, thus developing an integrated coal-and-salt enterprise - the usual pattern of development in the more advanced coal-producing areas in Fife and the Lothians.[3]

[1] *Old Statistical Account*
[2] Clerk of Penicuik MSS (SRO GD18/1069), Sir John Clerk: Dissertation
[3] Duckham, B.F. : *A History of the Scottish Coal Industry, Vol.1*

THE COALFIELD

Although the results of the survey carried out at Robert Cunninghame's request have not survived, the conclusions of another survey, undertaken nearly a century later, were incorporated in the Rev. Thomas Wodrow's report on the Parish of Stevenston (contained in Sir John Sinclair's Statistical Account of Scotland). This second survey established that there were eleven seams of coal lying in the area north of the sand-hills at Ardeer as well as between the coast and the River Garnock. The seams were of varying thickness and of different types. Because of the strike of the rock, seams dipped down towards the south-west and outcropped at intervals on moving inland from the coast. Numerous faults or fractures with some dislocation were indicated and the coalfield was divided into three by two dykes of igneous rock intruding into the sedimentary series.

The bigger of these two dykes is Capon Craig Gall, which is visible as a surface feature at some places along its length (e.g. between Boglemart Street and High Road, Stevenston. It is a twenty metre thick dyke of hard, impermeable whinstone which acted as a drainage barrier but did not disturb the rock strata, including the coal seams on either side of it. Inland from the Capon Craig Gall lay the Piper Heuch Gall, a thinner, less resistant dyke. Though it was less obvious above the surface, it had disturbed the strata round about, causing considerable dislocation.

Inland from Piper Heuch Gall, the seams became thinner, the quality of the coal in them decreased and the amount of faulting increased. A big fault known as the Mill-dam Step marked the eastern limit of workable coal. The basic reliability of the 1770 survey findings have been confirmed by more recent surveys, although the presence of some seams not previously recorded has been revealed.[1]

[1] Craig, G.E. (ed.): *The Geology of Scotland*

ROBERT CUNNINGHAME'S PIONEERING EFFORTS

We know from the First Statistical Account that one of Robert Cunninghame's first major projects was to initiate the driving of a drainage adit through his own estate and into that of his neighbour, the Earl of Eglinton. The purpose of the adit was to drain the coal seams that lay above it.

Essentially, a drainage adit was a gently inclined tunnel cut into the rock from a position low down on a slope where coal seams outcropped. It provided an escape route for water which would otherwise have gathered higher up in the coal workings, allowing it to run off freely. Sir John Clerk of Penicuik's advice on drainage adits was to make them about two feet wide, keeping them narrow to avoid roof collapse and to limit the cost of cutting them.[1]

Cunninghame's adit was a mile and a half long and cutting through solid rock and removing debris over that length must have been a long and difficult task. Brick-enforced ventilation shafts would have been added at intervals so that workers could continue cutting the adit. These served as access routes for the men working on the adit and as the means of removing the hewn rock. Work on the adit was completed in 1686 and its mouth, from which water still flows, can still be seen at the front in Melbourne Park in Saltcoats.

In the late 17th century, adits were not only cut for drainage purposes; they were the principal means of getting at below-the-surface coal. Miners cut into the seams where they outcropped on valley sides or hill slopes, and followed the strike of them underground. The roof of the mine was supported where necessary with timber, but it was the general practice to keep the passageway fairly narrow to cut down on the amount of support required. Where more substantial shoring was needed, at the entrance, for example, bricks and mortar were used.

Adit mines were known in Scotland as 'in gaun' e'en'. Each in gaun' e'e would be worked back as far as practical, with secondary tunnels cut at right angles into the surrounding coal, regulated in number and width by the need to leave sufficiently large amounts of coal untouched to prevent the roof collapsing.

When an in gaun' e'e was cut into a dipping seam, there was a tendency for water to collect in the lowest part of the mine. Eventually, the accumulated water would make it impossible for work to continue, and that in gaun' e'e would be abandoned in favour of a new one, starting further along the outcrop.

Cunninghame's long drainage adit cut down the problem of accumulating water in the in gaun' e'en on his own estate (and on the Earl of Eglinton's), meaning that the passageways had a longer life span, with less time and effort needed to get rid of water at the coalface. As a consequence, coal production increased.

Though the construction of the drainage adit improved conditions in some of the Stevenston coal workings, it could never be the complete solution on such a low-lying site. Other means of removing water had to be employed and Cunninghame was responsible for sinking The Deep Shank in the holm below Stevenston Parish Kirk (the concrete capping of that pit can still be seen). This was kept relatively free of water by harnessing some of the power of the Stevenston Burn. A water wheel wound up buckets full of water from the pit to the surface, where they were emptied into a runnel that drained into the burn.

Other pits, not conveniently placed near to a running stream that could be used to turn a water wheel, used horse-gins to wind up the buckets of water. Cunninghame operated at least two horse-gins and employed a total of sixteen horses, presumably working in teams of two on a rota basis.[2]

Neither the horse-gin nor the water wheel provided a really efficient means of getting rid of water. As the underground workings became more extensive and deeper, the problem of coping with the accumulating water grew, causing major operating difficulties for Cunninghame and his successors.

The horse-gins and the water wheel may also have been used at times to wind up the wrought coal from the bottom of the pit to the surface, supplementing the work of the bearers who carried loads of coal on their backs up a series of wooden ladders.

[1] Sir John Clerk: Dissertation
[2] *Old Statistical Account*

SALTCOATS HARBOUR

A key element in Robert Cunninghame's plan for the development of his part of the Stevenston coalfield was the exportation of coal to Ireland. To make coal exportation a possibility, he first had to find a place where boats could put in to be loaded. There was already a harbour at Irvine, but transporting Auchenharvie coal overland to it was too difficult because of the sandy terrain between Stevenston and Irvine. The alternative was to improve the facilities at Saltcoats Creek, which was much closer to where the coal was being produced.

It is known that before Robert Cunninghame's time small fishing boats used Saltcoats Creek, an inlet protected to the south by a narrow, rocky headland.[1] Whether or not the fishermen had improved upon nature by building a quay is not known, though it seems unlikely, as the scale of the fishing enterprise was small. Cunninghame proposed to build a harbour on this site and an Act of the Scottish Parliament of 1685 gave him permission to go ahead. This Act also allowed him to levy a charge of four pence Scots on every pint of beer sold within Saltcoats and Stevenston to help pay for the work.[2]

The building of the harbour was beset with difficulties. Each winter storms destroyed part of the work that had been carried out during the previous summer, and the task took fifteen years to complete. Even before it was finished, however, the harbour was an important outlet for Cunninghame's coal.

In Cunninghame's day, the marketing of coal was not the highly organised affair that it is today. The industry's commercial infra-structure had yet to be developed and Cunninghame had no big contracts to supply coal in agreed quantities to particular merchants in Ireland or Scotland. Instead the fuel was sold, load by load, at the pit head or coal ree and prices fluctuated as supply and demand varied from day to day. Some coal was sold at the pit head to satisfy local demand but much of it was sold at the harbour to the masters of vessels that put in there. If several put in at the same time, a good price could be commanded. These ships, loaded with the coal their masters had bought, then sailed to destinations in Ireland, selling their cargo for what they could get on the quay-side there.[3] The ships' masters needed commercial judgement and sound financial backing as well as navigational skills.

The ad hoc nature of coal marketing at the end of the 17th Century caused difficulties for coal consumers, and made it difficult for producers to plan ahead. Production could not be tailored to suit expected demand because demand varied, leading to fluctuation in prices and profitability.

[1] Pont, Timothy: *Cuninghame Topographised, 1604-1608*

[2] *Old Statistical Account*

[3] Vessels were required by law to discharge their cargo of coal within 10 days of arrival in harbour, perhaps to prevent masters withholding vital supplies in the hope of forcing the price up.

THE PRICE OF PROGRESS

Cunninghame's initial investments in the coalfield were on a grand scale and they appeared to be paying dividends as productivity increased. Indeed, his confidence in the continuing prosperity of the enterprise was shown by his building of a new family residence on the estate in 1708.[1]

However, uncertainties of the market, combined with operational difficulties encountered in the new mines, meant that Cunninghame's income was not sufficient to pay for all the developmental work without borrowing. There is no clear contemporary record of his growing indebtedness and information about Cunninghame's financial dealings only emerge in evidence brought forward in court cases after his own lifetime. That the court cases were necessary is indicative of the extreme complexity and obscurity of the financial arrangements surrounding the developments in the Stevenston coalfield. These developments were made at a time when there were no limited liability companies, no company law and the evolution of the Scottish banking system was only just beginning. Raising capital was done by involving friends and neighbours, using land and property as security.

Apparently, Cunninghame began by borrowing money from the Earl of Eglinton in 1683, but how much and on what security is not known[2]. In 1688 he entered into a Back Bond, a type of mortgage, with one of his neighbours, Mr Adam Campbell. In this way he secured access to £40,000 Scots with much of his land as security and he had the right to buy back the Bond at any time he was in a position to do so. But Mr Campbell sold off parts of the Bond to his son and to other neighbours which meant that Cunninghame had not one creditor but several and there was a danger that the situation could get out of hand. At some point the Earl of Eglinton either offered or was persuaded by Cunninghame to acquire the several parts of the Back Bond from their holders, thus becoming Cunninghame's sole creditor. While the coal enterprise flourished he could count on getting his interest paid and if it failed he could foreclose on the land itself. Rents paid by Cunninghame's tenants in Saltcoats were made over to Eglinton as part payment of the interest.

In 1707 Cunninghame sold the estate of Hullerhurst, part of his Barony of Stevenston, to William Kelso. A year later John Hamilton bought another part of the Barony, the estate of Grange, for an unknown sum. Around the same time Cunninghame sold the estate of Ardeer, nearly 1600 acres in extent, to the Reverend Patrick Warner, a veteran Covenanting minister who had spent some time in exile in the Low Countries, outlawed for preaching at Conventicles. The deal reserved Cunninghame the right to mine coal in Ardeer for the next 57 years. Clearly, Cunninghame was not interested in the land but in what was under it. Even so, the sum of £50 mentioned as changing hands between Warner and Cunninghame hardly seems a realistic price for a 1600 acre estate, even though much of it was covered in sand. As a copy of the original sasine cannot be traced, it is impossible to find out what exactly was going on, but the deal may have been a three-cornered one involving the Earl of Eglinton as well. If Ardeer was already included in the arrangements of the Back Bond, Cunninghame would not have been able to sell it to Warner without the Earl's consent, although he may have been able to persuade Eglinton that a sale would benefit all parties. Warner would get the land; the Earl would get the purchase price; Cunninghame would have his debts reduced and still have access to the coal. The £50 may have been a 'sweetener' paid to Cunninghame.

According to the Warner family papers, the deal made at the time of the sale did not allow Cunninghame free access to the coal in Ardeer.[3] Instead, it gave him the right to take a tack (or lease) of the coal bearing areas for 57 years. He was expected to pay Warner a fifth of the total sum he earned from the sale of coal brought up from the western part of the estate (where drainage difficulties made it harder to win the coal) and a quarter of the sum earned from the sale of coal wrought on the eastern part of the estate.

Whatever the exact details of the deal were, they were open to different interpretations by the parties involved. Those differences gave rise to the first of a long series of court cases which began not long after Robert Cunninghame's death.

[1] *New Statistical Account*

[2] The complicated story of Robert Cunninghame's indebtedness has been pieced together from several documents and memoranda in the Auchenharvie Papers, none of which are original agreements, but appear to date from the period after Robert Cunninghame's death.

[3] Scott, N.M. : "Documents relating to coal mining in the Saltcoats district in the first quarter of the Eighteenth Century.", *Scottish Historical Review 19* (1922)

ENTERPRISING GENIUS OR BANKRUPT FOOL?

Robert Cunninghame succeeded in establishing the biggest, most productive colliery in Ayrshire. In 1705 Spreull observed that "between fifty and sixty smacks plied regularly between Saltcoats and Dublin", carrying Cunninghame's coal to Ireland.[1] The dross and small coal, for which there was no other market, was used in the salt-pans for the production of sea-salt, for which there was a ready sale both locally and further afield for use in food preservation and the preparation of butter and cheese.

Yet, at the time of his death in 1715, Cunninghame was deeply in debt to the Earl of Eglinton. Had his investments in the colliery been wise? Did he over-estimate the potential of the coalfield, or had he expected the investments to be long term ones, with the financial rewards falling, not principally to himself, but to his children and grandchildren? He must have believed in the ultimate success of the colliery to have gone on investing in it over a number of years. His faith in its eventual financial viability must also have been shared by the Earl of Eglinton, who not only lent money to Robert Cunninghame but continued to lend to his heirs.

Cunninghame's reputation as an entrepreneur was high amongst his contemporaries and he was obviously held in great esteem by the Rev. Dr Wodrow who referred to him in the Old Statistical Account as "a very enterprising genius". However, with hindsight it is clear that he made errors of judgement in the development of the colliery, seriously underestimating the difficulties to be overcome in getting coal to the surface. Over-optimism was a common fault among coal proprietors who had no experience and little knowledge of mining.[2] Most of them were content to leave the physical and financial risks to others and leased out the coal seams on their land expecting immediate, short-term financial returns.

James Cunninghame died in 1728, leaving the Auchenharvie Estate and its atten-
dant financial mess to his son Robert, who was only eleven years old at the time. The
Peck partnership was no doubt glad of the chance to bow out of Stevenston and the
tack was transferred to Emmanuel Walker, a customs officer. During the short period
that he was in control a more efficient Newcomen engine was installed, thanks to Rob-
inson's appeal which had struck home, leading to twenty-three ship owners subscrib-
ing towards the purchase and installation of this engine. It was located at the Deep
Shank to the south of the High Stevenston Kirk and was operational by 1732.

Despite these apparent improvements to the fortunes of the Auchenharvie Estate,
its instability continued when the young Robert Cunninghame died a year later and
the estate passed to his three sisters. A valuation was carried out on behalf of the
three sisters, "the heirs portioner", and parts of the valuators' report relating to the
two pumping engines and to the saltpans have survived. The salt works seem to have
been in a semi-derelict condition at this time. If salt-making was not being carried out
on a regular basis, the poor quality dross (panwood) from the colliery would not have
had an economic use.

The three heirs portioner were advised to appoint a manager, and John Cunninghame, a local ship master - not related to the young Cunninghame ladies - became
manager and factor of the colliery. However, it transpired that he, too, was unable to
run the enterprise at a profit.[6]

VALUATION OF A STEAM PUMP

by Thomas Reid, Merchant, and George Cunninghame,
Manager of the Coal Works at Eglinton. Commission from
John Cunninghame, Shipmaster, the Factor for Managing the
Coal Works belonging to the heirs of the Deceased J. Cunninghame.

The Fire Engine Boiler	£14 sterling
Iron Works	47/9/1
Cylinder	20/-/-
Bottom of Cylinder	24/-/-
Regulator	3/-/-
Rest	9/16/4
Valves, Cocks, etc.	6/16/-
Lead Work	42/-/-
Beams & Frames	9/17/-
Pump Rods	2/3/-
Pipes	53/-/-
Wooden Jack Staves	5/16/-

TOTAL	£239/08/-
	If moved would be £139

[1] *New Statistical Account*
[2] Hume, J.R.: *The Industrial Archaeology of Scotland, Vol. 1*
[3] *New Statistical Account*
[4] Whatley, C.A.: *The Finest Place for a Lasting Colliery*
[5] Carlisle Records Office, Lowther MSS. D/hons/W.Misc.
[6] Eglinton v Cunninghame, 1747

PROFITS AND PROBLEMS

In 1737, Anna, the eldest of the three sisters married John Reid, the second son of the Reverend William Reid who was minister of Stevenston Parish. John Reid took over the running of the Auchenharvie Estate. He was already a merchant and seems to have brought a great deal of business acumen into the management of Auchenharvie affairs. Little evidence survives in the Auchenharvie Papers of his early efforts but he must have installed two more pumping engines before 1747 when the installation of a "fifth engine" is recorded. He must also have restored the saltpans to working order to allow salt to be produced by burning the otherwise useless panwood, as a "General Ballance" sheet drawn up in 1761 shows that between 1749 and 1761 the colliery and salt works combined made a profit of £3,236. Not exactly a fortune for a twelve year period, but a considerable improvement on what had gone before. In 1756 he bought out the interests of the other two heirs portioner in the agricultural lands of the estate though Elizabeth, who was unmarried, and Barbara, who had married William Cunninghame of Kilwinning, continued to have rights in the colliery, saltpans and harbour. In 1761 John Reid was able to lease the colliery and saltpans to another Stevenston merchant, Alexander Crawford, on terms appropriate for a modestly profitable enterprise.

Auchenharvie interests appeared to be prospering, but what of the debt to the Earl of Eglinton? Alexander, the ninth Earl, with whom Robert Cunninghame and his son James Cunninghame had dealings, died in 1729. That was just a year after James Cunninghame's untimely death which left his 11 year old son as heir to Auchenharvie. Alexander was succeeded by his son, also called Alexander, who became the tenth Earl of Eglinton, known in his day as a great agricultural improver.

> ....great praise is due to the proprietors of Ayrshire for their
> very successful exertions in enclosing their lands and in
> embellishing the whole country with plantations. In these
> great points none displayed more taste, or made greater
> exertions, at so early a period, as Alexander, the tenth Earl of
> Eglinton...[1]

(Alexander was fatally wounded on 24th October 1769 in a dispute with Mungo Campbell, an exciseman whom he had accused of poaching.)

The agricultural improvements pioneered by Alexander opened up the market for lime, used to neutralise the acidity of Ayrshire soils. Lime burning created a new market for low grade coal which could be used in lime kilns.

It is difficult to make sense of the papers relating to the debts owed by the Cunninghames to the Eglintons as there is a great deal of variation between the sums mentioned from paper to paper. The variation is due, at least in part, to the fact that sums are reckoned in pounds Scots in the early papers. The Act of Union of 1707 abolished the Scottish currency. The pound Scots was valued at 1/12 of the pound sterling at that time. In papers dated after 1707, it seems that sums were being reckoned sometimes in pounds Scots, sometimes in pounds sterling. The situation is further complicated by the reckoning of sums in marks or merks, an older unit of currency which was worth 13/4 (13 shillings and 4 pence) or two thirds of the pound Scots. The papers for the most part are personal letters and terms like "bond", "rent", and "interest" are used without the precision that would be expected in legal documents.

It seems that the total indebtedness to the Ninth Earl of Eglinton at the time of Robert Cunninghame's death in 1719 was in the region of £22,200 Scots. This was made up of sums borrowed directly from him by Cunninghame to help pay for work on the harbour at Saltcoats and the development of the coalworkings, and sums that the Earl had paid to acquire portions of the "back bond" from Cunninghame's other creditors. Repayment of the debt, with interest at 5%, was made through the payment of the tack (or rent) for the Auchenharvie coal workings directly to the Earl as well as the payment of rents for land and houses in Saltcoats (and Townhead Stevenston) belonging to the Cunninghames, again directly to the Earl. This arrangement continued from 1719 until 1728, reducing the debt to £7,332 Scots.

In 1725 the Earl of Eglinton demanded that James Cunninghame make over to him permanently the whole of Saltcoats and threatened to foreclose on the debt if this was not done. Cunninghame implored the Earl not to throw him and his family out on the streets, writing to him in impassioned terms about the suffering his family would endure if he were to give up Saltcoats entirely. The Earl evidently relented and paid out in the same year a further sum of £360 on Cunninghame's behalf to Mr. Warner of Ardeer in settlement of a law suit concerning the coal workings in Ardeer.

The arrangements for clearing the debt fell into abeyance in 1728 at James Cunninghame's death. The coal workings were no longer being leased out so there was no tack being paid, but the Earl continued to receive the rents for Saltcoats, as did Alexander the tenth Earl who succeeded to the Eglinton Estate in 1729. It was he who initiated a law suit against the heirs portioner of the Cunninghame family for the recovery of the debt in 1747. The tenth Earl was pressing for the making over of Saltcoats to him to settle the outstanding debt. A statement of the debt in connection with the case was jotted down in 1750:

Due to the Earl at Martinmas 1728	£7,332
Rent (interest) thereof Mart 1728 to Whit 1750	7,882
To Mr. Warner, Decrete Arbital of Lord Grange of Dun	360
Rent thereof Whit 1725 to Whit 1750	450
1000 mark bond by Auchenharvie to E. of E.	666
Rent thereof from Sept. 1709 to Whit 1750	1,319
Year's tack duty of Raise Mine	66
Rent thereof from Mart 1734 to Whit 1750	51
	18,128 Scots

Less	
The whole rental of Saltcoats and Townhead	
after deducting sums paid for house repairs	
and half the schoolmaster's salary annually	£7,702
	10,426
Rent (interest) from Whit to Mart 1750	- 260
Due to the Earl at Martinmas 1750	10,686

The above figures are all in pounds Scots, although technically pounds Scots had been obsolete for 43 years.

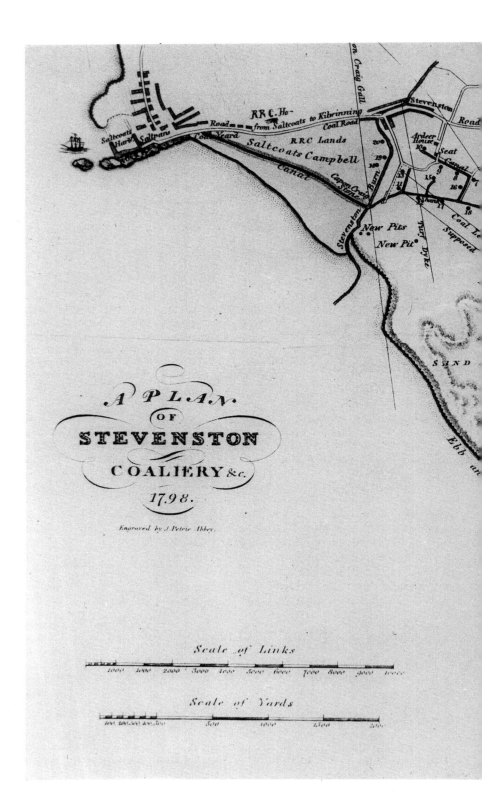

A PLAN

OF

STEVENSTON

COALIERY &c.

1798.

Engraved by J. Petrie Abbey.

Scale of Links

Scale of Yards

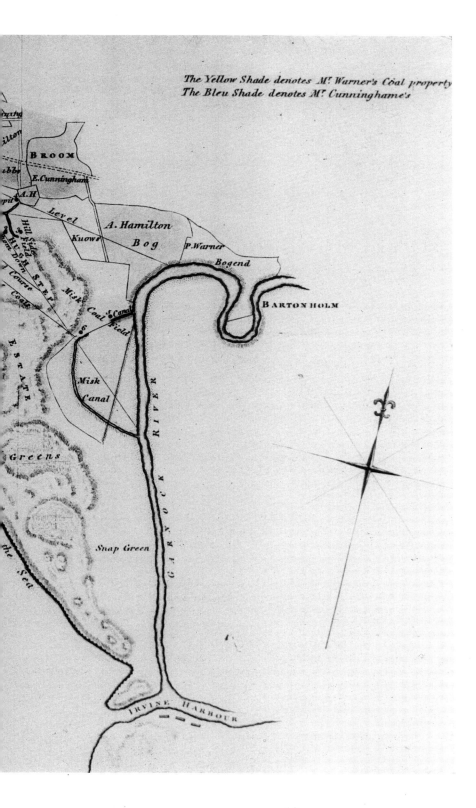

The Yellow Shade denotes M.ʳ Warner's Coal property
The Bleu Shade denotes M.ʳ Cunninghame's

BROOM

E. Cunningham

A.H

Level

Kuows

A. Hamilton

Bog

P. Warner

Bogend

BARTON HOLM

Hill Side Field

Broom Down

STEP

Misk

Coal Canal Field

Misk Canal

ESTATE

Greens

GARNOCK RIVER

Snap Green

the Sea

IRVINE HARBOUR

19

The tenth Earl got what he wanted. Certain lands in Saltcoats were made over to the Eglinton Estate while the Auchenharvie Estate retained the land around the harbour and the saltpans. It may have seemed simple and straightforward at the time, but the land division created problems later on when John Reid's son, Robert Reid Cunninghame wanted to build a waggon way to transport coal to the harbour. There was a disagreement about what land by the shore belonged to whom and further legal wrangling ensued.

[1] Robertson, G.: *Rural Recollections*

ROBERT REID CUNNINGHAME

In 1770 John and Anna Reid's son, Robert, took over the running of the coal working enterprise although he was still a young man. The agreement of the heirs portioner had been sought and obtained. To re-enforce the continuity of the family's interest Robert Reid added Cunninghame to his name. He seems to have inherited his great grandfather's enthusiasm and breadth of vision and he made the successful running of the coal works and related business his life's work. His approach was radically different from that of many of his contemporaries, who regarded coal reserves on their land as just one of many resources to be exploited as and when needed, with as little inconvenience and as little investment of their own money and effort as possible. Robert Reid Cunninghame threw himself wholeheartedly into the business, much as his great grandfather had done and he made it his profession.

In the description of Stevenston parish contained in the New Statistical Account, Dr Landsborough calls Robert Reid Cunninghame an "enterprising and successful manager" who acted with "judgement and spirit". He certainly transformed the financial situation at Auchenharvie, making the colliery into a thoroughly profitable business. The Auchenharvie Papers reveal him as a hard-headed, determined man with a ruthless streak. Perhaps it is impossible to succeed in business without a certain ruthlessness. He was often at loggerheads with his neighbours and partners and, as a result, became involved in several law suits with them.

Like his great grandfather, he saw that profitability depended on running a large integrated enterprise, concerned, not merely with getting coal to the surface, but with organising its transportation and marketing locally and abroad. As the 57 year leasing arrangements concerning coal reserves in Ardeer, made between Robert Cunninghame and Patrick Warner at the time of the sale of Ardeer, had run out in 1765, Robert Reid Cunninghame began by forming a partnership (or co-partnery as it was called) with Warner of Ardeer. This allowed Robert to continue coal extraction there as well as on his own land, maintaining the business as a large-scale operation with himself as manager. The co-partnery was later referred to as the Stevenston Coal Company although it was not a limited liability company as we understand it. The partners contributed coal-bearing lands that were to be worked as a single entity.

Realising the necessity of continuing the sale of coal to the Irish market, he carried out improvement work at Saltcoats harbour. Saltcoats was the principal coal port on the Clyde at this time, with sailings continuing throughout the winter months. Passage in and out of the harbour could be assisted by a warping capstan or winch. Its position allowed ships sea-room to make their way from the harbour against the prevailing westerly winds. Unlike other Ayrshire harbours, it was not at a river-mouth and there was no off-shore sand bar to be negotiated or to restrict the draught of vessels that could use the harbour. Though part of the basin formed by the pier built out along the Shott dried out at each low tide, there was room for 30 vessels. Even so, there were often "queues" of vessels waiting to be loaded.[1]

To ease the congestion the quay was extended along the Shott, providing tying-up space for many more ships and those of deeper draught. A much more elaborate plan shown in the Old Statistical Account never came to fruition as it involved building quays on the north side of the basin on land belonging to the Eglinton estate. The Eglinton and Auchenharvie families became involved in litigation over disputed territory and the Earl of Eglinton eventually opted for the creation of a new harbour at Ardrossan.[1]

With these improvements, Saltcoats continued to be the main coal exporting port on the Ayrshire coast for some time and Cunninghame, shrewd business man that he was, had a financial interest in several of the coal boats that sailed from Saltcoats.

The coal boats were not all that big, between 70 and 90 tons burthen, with holds that took about 300 cart loads of coal. The coal was barrowed on by labourers. Experienced masters paid the labourers a bit extra to ensure that the load was evenly distributed. Once loaded, the boats had to make their way to the Royal Burgh of Irvine to get customs clearance. The Dublin bound boats sailed down the coast, sometimes putting in at Stranraer to take on stores which were reputedly cheaper there than in Saltcoats. The crossing from Stranraer to Dublin could take five days, depending on wind and weather. The boats often had to wait their turn to be unloaded. According to a regulation they were supposed to be unloaded within 10 days of arrival. The regulation may have been intended to ensure that there were no hold-ups in supply caused by masters withholding their cargo in the hope of getting a better price. Alternatively, it may have been a response to the fear of spontaneous combustion in coal cargoes.

The return journey to Saltcoats was often made with limestone as the pay load. The limestone was most likely destined for agricultural use after treatment in coal-burning limekilns. (Evidence of some of these limekilns is still to be seen around Saltcoats. There is one, for example, about half a mile from Ardrossan Cemetery on the Sorbie Road.) Some boats stayed in harbour from December to early April. Others continued to make crossings in spite of the hazards.

Although the coal trade with Dublin accounted for most of the activity at Saltcoats Harbour, vessels from Saltcoats also sailed to Scandinavia, France, Portugal, and Newfoundland, bringing back cargoes of commodities ranging from timber to rum. Saltcoats was also the home port for several herring busses.[3]

While Cunninghame's work at the harbour had gone some way to easing the congestion there, he still had to contend with the problem of getting coal from the pit heads to the harbour and nearby saltpans, not an easy task given the sandy nature of the terrain in between as it would have been difficult for horses to get any purchase on the deep sand. As a result, cart-loads were small, probably about 5 or 6 hundred-weights. Robert considered several ways round the problem and decided that the best option was to construct a canal.

The canal was finished and navigated September 19, 1772, the
first upon which any business was done in Scotland. It is a
ditch without any locks, but very wide and deep in some places
from inequality of the ground; 2 miles long, besides the
long side branches afterwards cut to the mouth of every new
pit that opened; twelve feet wide at the bottom, the sides
inclined at an angle of 45 degrees; the water four feet deep;
the boats carry for the shipping or the saltpans, from twelve to
fifteen tons.[4]

Depth of water was controlled through a spill dam on the Stevenston Burn where
the canal crossed the burn and water pumped out of the coal pits was fed into the
canal.

The building of the canal enhanced Robert's growing reputation and gave Auchenharvie the edge once more over other collieries in technical innovation. It was a major
undertaking requiring capital investment from the co-partnery on a big scale. Patrick
Warner of Ardeer, Cunninghame's partner, was involved financially and Patrick's
brother, John, who was actually the minister of Kilbarchan, supervised the work. He
had previously been involved in the drainage work carried out at Castle Semple for
William McDowall and brought experienced men with him to work on the project.[5] It
is possible that John Warner inherited an interest in water-control work from his
grandfather, the Covenanting minister who may have learned about drainage tech-
niques during his exile in Holland and had transformed land he owned near Irvine
from moss to arable land.[6]

Constructing the canal was a laborious business. As it was being cut through sand
and sandy soil, clay had to be carted to the site to make the puddled clay with which
the bottom and sides of the canal had to be lined. Then there was the problem of the
hard igneous rock of the Shott, the rocky outcrop which provided the base for the harbour and which continued inland (in geological terms it is an intruded dyke). It proved
to be either too difficult or too expensive to cut through, with the result that the canal
came to an end about 600 yards from the harbour. Coal had to be unloaded from the
canal barges into horse-drawn carts for the final quarter of a mile journey from the
pits to the harbour or the pans, adding significantly to the total cost of transport. The
cost of the canal was £4857/4/-, the bill being paid by the Stevenston Coal Company.

Even so, it was the "most complete water system of colliery transport ever devised in
Britain".[7] Cunninghame had eight barges specially built for use on his canal and he
claimed that one such vessel carried as much as could be carried by fifty horses and
carts. He also claimed that the colliery was losing money until the canal came into
operation.[8]

[1] Graham, E.J.: *The Shipping Trade of Ayrshire 1689-1791*
[2] Levy, Catriona: *Ardrossan Harbour*
[3] Graham, E.J.: op cit
[4] *Old Statistical Account*
[5] Duckham, B.F. : *A History of the Scottish Coal Industry, Vol.1*
[6] Robertson, G.: *A Genealogical Account of The Principal Families in Ayrshire, Vol. 1*
[7] Duckham, B. F: op. cit.
[8] Court of Session Productions: Warner v Cunninghame Nos. 638-9, excs 231/Misc. 26/1

BREAKING NEW GROUND

Some time prior to 1778 the co-partnery commissioned a new survey of the coalfield. The results of this survey form the basis of the description of the coalfield found in the Old Statistical Account. By this time such surveys were much more reliable than the hit-or-miss affairs of a hundred years earlier and the information brought to light by this survey led to the sinking of a trial pit at the eastern boundary of Warner's Ardeer estate. The coal there was found to be of good quality and the Misk Colliery was opened up. The main shaft was 240 feet deep and gave access to two workable seams. It was drained by a steam engine and proved to be very productive. There was, however, the problem of transporting the coal from the Misk, across the sandhills of Ardeer, towards Saltcoats.

Robert Reid Cunninghame had the ingenious idea of trying to link up the Misk pit with the coal workings to the north by a narrow underground canal that utilised the space where coal had been extracted. The route was actually pushed two hundred yards towards the Misk by removing coal. However, this coal degenerated into poor quality, unsaleable stuff, which the Old Statistical Account calls "Humph". The plan was abandoned and instead two short canals were dug connecting the two pit heads at Misk with the River Garnock. These short waterways of 250 and 80 yards length had lock gates where they entered the river. Lighters capable of carrying 30 tons of coal were built. They could be loaded at the pit heads by emptying the baskets of coal coming out of the pit straight into their holds. The lighters made their way along the canals into the Garnock and down the river into Irvine Bay, where their cargoes were discharged into coal boats at Irvine Harbour. These coal boats could only take on a part load as they were unable to cross a sand bar at the mouth of the harbour carrying a full load, but once over the bar they could take on more coal from the lighters. Also, the operation could not be carried out in bad weather. In spite of the limitations, an average of 10,000 tons of coal a year was transported from the Misk colliery into Irvine Bay during the 1780s.

New pits were opened up near the older workings as well, although there were difficulties caused by the depth of unconsolidated sand. Wide circles had to be cleared of sand and enclosed with shuttering to keep the sand from slipping back while the work proceeded downwards towards the more solid clay soil where a proper re-inforced pit mouth could be constructed. The Reverend Mr Wodrow describes in the Old Statistical Account an occasion when 300 men worked night and day to clear sand to a depth of 36 feet before clay was reached.

Each of the new pits was connected to the main canal. By 1790 this part of the coalfield was producing a yearly average of 13,000 tons and new pumping engines were installed.[1] Another innovation made by Robert Reid Cunninghame was the installation of a Boulton and Watt rotative engine for winding loads of coal up from the bottom of the pit shaft. Boulton and Watt's patent produced a far more efficient engine than earlier adaptations of the Newcomen engine for circular movement. The first steam winding engine used in the Stevenston collieries was installed in 1802 and cost £1,704.[2] It may well have been the first Boulton and Watt engine in use in Scotland.[3]

Despite these developments, Robert Reid Cunninghame did not neglect the salt-making part of the enterprise. He had a new saltpan built, probably in 1787 or 1788, bringing the total of working pans up to four. They were close to the harbour and drew their sea-water from a single reservoir. Together they sold about 3,000 bolls of salt a year. (A boll was a Scots dry measure of capacity roughly equivalent to 145 litres.)

The Earl of Eglinton also had saltpans in operation close to the harbour at Saltcoats. Both salt works were within the Irvine Precinct for tax purposes and the owners had to pay, on a quarterly basis, the Salt Tax Officer at Irvine the sums due on the salt sold. The duty varied according to whether the salt was exported, traded along the coast, or retailed where it was produced. The quarterly salt tax vouchers give a record of how much salt was sold but actual output figures have to be estimated as the storage of salt, even over a relatively short period, involves some loss due to the deliquescent nature of salt. Efficient marketing was therefore essential and Cunninghame's saltpans produced over 80% of salt sales in Ayrshire in the last decade of the 18th century. Unlike other saltpans, those at Saltcoats worked continuously, there being no interruptions in the supply of coal. They were considered relatively productive as it was reckoned that 1lb of salt was produced from 25 lbs of water.[3] (This figure, however, was somewhat exaggerated as contemporary figures indicate that 25 lbs of salt water would contain 0.875 lbs of solids of which only 0.68 lbs would be salt. Therefore, 35-40lbs of water would actually need to be evaporated to produce 1lb of salt.)

Although Saltcoats lies at some distance from the mouth of a major river, the salt workers were aware that the 25:1 ratio altered quite considerably during what they called "freshes" - periods when prolonged rain led to increased discharges of fresh water from local burns and more distant rivers. Most of the salt produced seems to have been sold locally, probably for use mainly in butter and cheese making, though some of it would also have been used in fish curing and for domestic purposes.

[1] *Old Statistical Account*
[2] Court of Session Productions: Warner v Cunninghame Nos. 638-9, excs 231/Misc. 26/1
[3] B. F. Duckham: op. cit., p110
[4] Report on Coalworks & Saltworks by John Clerk & John Roebuck, made in connection with Warner v Cunninghame case CS 3086

THE FOLLY OF LITIGATION

Not everything went Robert Reid Cunninghame's way. In spite of all his initiative and expertise in overcoming technical and logistical difficulties, he had obstacles of another kind blocking his path to success and fortune - his neighbours.

In 1805 one of them, the Earl of Eglinton, turnpiked the public road which ran through his estate to the village of Saltcoats and the harbour there. That meant that Eglinton was given permission, through an Act of Parliament, to take over from the local Justices of the Peace who had been responsible for the upkeep of the road. Instead of relying on Statute Labour (requiring local men to give their labour free for a few days a year in order to keep the road passable), Eglinton supplied his own men and materials to keep the road in good repair. To re-coup the cost Eglinton was empowered to charge road-users a toll. This was levied at toll barriers along the length of the road. When the appropriate tolls had been paid, the barrier was turned to allow vehicles to pass. One such toll barrier was located in what is now Canal Street, not far from Cunninghame's coal ree.

Cunninghame thus had to pay to transport his coal the short distance from the coal yard at the end of his canal to the harbour. He paid a sum of £30 a year to Eglinton instead of having to put up with the inconvenience of paying for each cart load separately. In 1811 Eglinton increased the toll charges in the wake of new legislation. He wrote to Cunninghame informing him that he would now be expected to pay £300 per annum. Not surprisingly, Cunninghame was shocked and angry at the increase and he began thinking about alternative ways of getting his coal to the harbour. He took legal advice about the possibility of building his own road, but he was advised that this would be illegal. His solution was to construct a waggon way.

A waggon way was a permanent way that used wooden rails, kept in position by stone sleeper blocks, to guide the wheels of waggons pulled by horses. The waggons ran on the rails, making the work of the horses pulling heavy loads much easier as well as preventing the ground from churning up. The route that Cunninghame took for his waggon way was along the rocks of the foreshore but the Earl of Eglinton disputed his ownership of this area. The land adjacent to it had come into Eglinton's hands through Warner's failure to redeem a mortgage on it, and he claimed that the foreshore was his as well. Cunninghame's case was that the foreshore had not been part of the deal made between Robert Cunninghame and Patrick Warner in 1708 and therefore could not have been part of the later mortgage arrangement between Warner and Eglinton. A court interdict was applied for in the names of the Earl and Countess of Eglinton, and also some of the free-holders of Saltcoats with houses near the shore, who argued that the building of a waggon way would cut off their access to the shore, stopping them gathering stones and preventing them taking their horses down to the sea to wash their feet.

An interdict was granted to allow all parties to be heard but was recalled after a few months. Meanwhile, Cunninghame continued work on the waggon way and by 1812 it was completed up to the Saracen's Head Inn. The Earl and his fellow litigants took no further action at this time and after a year and a day the case was deemed to have been "Let Sleep". (The dispute over the ownership of the foreshore arose again later when a branch line of the steam railway to Saltcoats Harbour was being considered and it was not until 1853 that a final pronouncement of who owned what was made in the Court of Session.)

In the meantime the waggon way was in continuous use. The purpose built waggons were owned by the colliery, which also owned 50 horses.[1] Twenty of them were used underground while others were employed in the gins that pumped water out of the pits. Some may also have been available for towing barges on the canal or for pulling the waggons, which could carry loads of roughly two tons, but much of the haulage work was contracted out.[2]

[1] *Old Statistical Account*
[2] Court of Session Productions: Warner v Cunninghame, No. 638 - 9

MORE TROUBLE AHEAD

Robert Reid Cunninghame's legal dispute with his neighbour, Eglinton, was only a mild skirmish compared to the prolonged battle that went on between him and the son of his neighbour and partner, Patrick Warner. They were litigious times certainly, though Cunninghame seems to have been involved in more than his fair share of unsought litigation. Were his neighbours motivated by jealousy of his apparent success, or had his single-minded pursuit of commercial success made him abrasive and difficult to get on with?

His partner was the grandson of the Reverend Patrick Warner, the Covenanting minister who acquired Ardeer in 1708. This Patrick Warner (whose mother was a Hamilton of Grange, to which family Robert Reid Cunninghame's first wife also belonged) was born in 1712 and was already an elderly man when the co-partnery was formed. His role within the co-partnery was unlikely to have been an active one. The description of the developments at the colliery in the Old Statistical Account is a contemporary account compiled when Robert Reid Cunninghame was still to the fore. In it, Cunninghame is credited with master-minding all the innovations and improvements, while Warner is merely named as his co-partner. But Cunninghame could not do without Warner because much of the coal was, after all, under Warner's land. Warner, for his part, seems to have been happy enough to leave the management of the colliery in the enthusiastic hands of the younger, more active, and undoubtedly more capable man.

But his son, also named Patrick, had other ideas. He seems to have been convinced that Cunninghame was cheating the Warners. By 1792, Patrick Warner, the elder, was no longer capable of handling his own affairs and his son persuaded him to accept the appointment of a Curator Bonis to act on his behalf. The Curator Bonis, presumably at the son's instigation, immediately raised court actions against Cunninghame. The actions called for a reckoning of the colliery profits over the years since the co-partnery was formed and the abandonment of all agreements made between Warner and Cunninghame on the grounds of fraud by Cunninghame and on account of Warner's "facility" (i.e. his senility).

The Curator Bonis proposed that while the action was pending in the court, Cunninghame should stand down as manager and that the management of the colliery should be put in the hands of a Mr. Russell, who was a ship master, and a Mr. Miller, who was a preacher. The proposal was rejected in the strongest terms by Cunninghame, who thought it preposterous that the management of a colliery which he had built into a successful and profitable business over many years should be taken over by two men who knew nothing whatsoever about mining.

The legal processes rumbled on for over twenty years and there are close on two thousand hand-written pages of evidence produced by the parties to the case and the experts called in as witnesses on their behalf.[1] These included smiths, carters, colliers and wrights, and acknowledged experts of the time on mining matters, like John Clerk and John Roebuck who reported on the colliery and saltworks in 1799. They thought that the enterprise was in excellent shape and was likely to do even better in the future if only "the folly of litigation" could be retracted.

The first decision, made at local level, found in favour of Warner, but Cunninghame immediately appealed against it. The case was then prolonged first by the death in

1795 of the elder Patrick Warner, and secondly by the death of the judge hearing the appeal, Lord Abercrombie.

In the meantime, Warner's lawyer made several propositions to Cunninghame in the hope of circumventing further legal procedures. It was suggested in 1798 that each party should take back their own property and go their separate ways. Cunninghame refused. He turned down another proposition in 1799 that the whole concern should be let out to the highest bidder and he rejected Warner's offer made in 1800 of £2,000 plus the Misk Farm for his part of the business. Throughout this Cunninghame continued to manage the colliery and in due course a new judge, Lord Meadowbank, was appointed and the appeal hearing began afresh.

The original agreement made between Robert Reid Cunninghame and the elder Patrick Warner had been to mine coal and to make salt for twenty-five years, each party specifying the coal-bearing lands on their respective estates to be included in the agreement. Cunninghame was to be manager for life. The agreement was enlarged in 1783 (long before the expiry of the original 25 year term) and both parties put in more coal-bearing land. The agreement was arranged to last until 1869.

Before beginning to take evidence at the hearing, Lord Meadowbank decreed that:

1. Patrick Warner (son) was bound to fulfil his father's lawful engagements.

2. It was lawful for Cunninghame to be appointed manager for life, and the agreement could not be broken just because relations between the partners were not cordial.

3. The partnership could only be dissolved if it could be shown that the agreement had been come to by deception.

[1] The documents relating to the Warner v Cunninghame case: Court of Session Productions Nos. 638-9, ex CS.231/Misc.26/1 2221 ex CS.238/Misc.25/5 3085-6 ex process CS.235/W23/5

CLAIMS AND COUNTERCLAIMS

A key point in Warner's case was his claim that a great deal more Warner land had been included in the agreement than Cunninghame had contributed. Cunninghame conceded that this was true, but argued that the co-partnery's resources should not be reckoned simply in terms of coal bearing land. He had contributed the harbour, the canal, and the saltworks, which were essential to the success of the enterprise.

Warner claimed that most of the coal mined by the co-partnery up to that time had come from his ground. Cunninghame, while agreeing that this was true for the first twenty years of the co-partnery's activities, pointed out that the proportion of coal mined on Cunninghame land had increased over the past eight years and would increase still more in the future. He claimed that out of a total production of 153,000 tons, 52,000 tons had come from Cunninghame ground.

Warner further claimed that it was unreasonable that Cunninghame should have been made manager for life. Cunninghame defended his record as manager, and stated that he had never taken any payment for his managerial work, being content with his share of the profits.

Attacking Cunninghame's record as manager, Warner claimed that the canal was a failure economically. Although the cost per ton of transporting coal along the canal was only 3d, it cost another 8d per ton to transfer it from barge to cart and transport it from the end of the canal to either the harbour or the saltworks. The transfer of the coal, Warner alleged, caused breakage and damage so that a lot of good coal was rendered unfit for sale to Ireland and thus had to be used in the saltworks.

To this Cunninghame argued that the canal was a financial success as the cost of transporting coal on it was less, even allowing for the cost of cartage over the last quarter of a mile to the harbour, than they had paid for cartage before the canal had been dug. Then they had had to pay between 1/8d and 2/-d per ton.

Cunninghame was also accused of not charging an economic price for the coal used at the saltworks. He thought that the small coal's market price ought to be around 6/- per ton. Working on that basis the saltworks would have been running at a loss, which over the years would have amounted to £6,832.

Cunninghame refuted Warner's claim that the market price for the small coal or panwood was 6/- per ton. He pointed out that had it not been for the saltworks, there would have been little or no demand for the panwood and they would have been left with tons of it unsold. By his reckoning, over the 28 years of the co-partnery, the saltworks had realised a profit of £18,611.

The lack of agreement about what the profits or losses over the years had been highlighted Warner's claim that the co-partnery's books were in such a mess that it was impossible to get an accurate view of the financial position. He pointed out that the accounts had not been certified annually by Mr Warner (senior). Cunninghame argued that the books were put in the possession of Mr Warner once a year and, in any case, he had been free to inspect them whenever he came to dine at Seabank. However, the old man had not thought to sign them to show his acceptance of them until the 12th year of the agreement. Mr Coventry, manager of Shewalton Colliery, testified on Cunninghame's behalf that the books had been properly kept.

Warner accused Cunninghame of having misappropriated money and materials belonging to the co-partnery in order to build his house at Seabank and to construct various farm buildings on his estate. This accusation was strenuously denied by Cunninghame and he pointed out that the apparent lack of profitability in the first years of the co-partnery had been the result of capital expenditure soaking up the profits, but since 1799 the partners had received an annual share-out of £750 each.

In a document drawn up in 1806, when Cunninghame was fighting to get legal costs from Warner, there is a resume of all the pits sunk, engines installed and improvements made over the 36 years since the co-partnery was entered into. It is an impressive list:

> 25 Pits put down and all succeeded to utmost expectation, not
> one of them misgave.
> 7 Engines (Steam) erected.

3 Rotative Machines and Gigs erected.
2 Saltpans erected all anew.
A canal cut and put to use and a harbour constructed in four
months for the great benefit of the Coaliery and all this
done in the course of 36 years.
The great exertions, fatigue of body and mind during that
time may be conceived by those experienced in Coalieries,
together with the great attention required in the
management of such extensive Operations.

Those "experienced in Coalieries" who were called as witnesses in the Appeal case gave it as their opinion that the mining of Warner's coal-bearing land and Cunninghame's coal-bearing land was carried out most economically as one enterprise because the land was essentially part of the same coalfield. They pointed out that as the seams of coal on Warner's land were lower than on Cunninghame's land, water would tend to gravitate towards the workings on Warner's land. Any attempt to mine there as a separate enterprise would have landed Warner in serious difficulties with drainage.

If the co-partnery had not existed, they argued, Cunninghame would not have been obliged to use Warner's small coal in the saltpans and Warner would probably have been unable to sell it at all. Much of the coal mined on Warner's land was transported over Cunninghame's land. Without Cunninghame's goodwill, Warner would have had problems with transportation.

The Appeal judge, Lord Meadowbank upheld the Appeal, vindicating Cunninghame's management of the co-partnery, and agreeing with his case in almost every detail. Costs were awarded to Cunninghame, but the court's findings stated that the actual amount of the costs should be decided elsewhere. That was the cue for further litigation - Cunninghame had another fight on his hands to recover his costs.

Although the legal judgement cleared Cunninghame of any deception in the setting up of the co-partnery, it is possible to feel a certain amount of sympathy for Warner's son. Though his father was quite happy not to be directly involved in coal mining at Ardeer, it would have been a frustrating situation for a young active man who had ideas of his own about how the business should be run, but no opportunity to put his ideas into practice. From the wording of some of the proposals made to Cunninghame while the court case was in progress, it looks as if Warner wanted to try his own hand at management.

There is evidence that Warner did try to interfere in the running of the pits by giving orders to John Auld, the overseer. When Auld pointed out that he took his orders from Cunninghame, Warner lost his temper and shouted at him. Cunninghame rallied to Auld's defence writing to Warner in polite but firm terms regarding an incident that occurred in 1806:

The repeated abuse and threatening to John Auld, our
principal oversman when you meet him at the pits, is attended
with very bad consequences, and, if continued in, will be very
hurtful to the Coalery, by creating amongst the Coaliers, a
disrespect and disregard to him as oversman.
During my management of the Coalery I have had many

Greeves and Oversmen, good, bad and indifferent, but I'll venture to say, and prove, that those employed at present and for a considerable time past, on the strictest investigation, will be found to merit regard, rather than threats, and particularly from one who has reaped such benefits through their good conduct in every respect.

Auld was in an unenviable pig-in-the-middle situation as relations worsened between Robert Reid Cunninghame and Patrick Warner. He was obviously held in high regard by Cunninghame, but leased the house he lived in in Stevenston from Warner. In September 1811 Warner actually stopped masons employed by Auld carrying out repairs already begun to the back wall of the house for no better reason than to spite Auld, whom he believed had threatened one of the "coaliers", Joseph Hunter, with dismissal if he carried tales about what happened at the pit to Warner. The two men, Auld and Warner, met "upon the coal hill of the Park pit" and a nasty little scene ensued. Warner accused Auld of lying during a hearing of the Cunninghame v Warner Appeal and with threatening other men with dismissal if they did not testify as he directed them. When Auld denied this and insisted that he had not prevented Hunter speaking to Warner but had advised him to tell the truth, Warner flew into a rage. He threatened Auld that if he stopped any man giving him information about the work, "God dam his soul, he would knock him down or shoot him." Three witnesses confirmed the goings-on at the coal hill, but there is no further information about what happened to the house repairs.

The case that Warner made out against Cunninghame may have been rejected by Lord Meadowbank, but it was not entirely without foundation. Over two-thirds of the coal mined by the co-partnery undeniably came from Warner's ground. There was a long period when Warner (senior) got no return for his investment. In spite of the testimony of accredited experts of the time as to the accuracy of Cunninghame's book-keeping, well-qualified accountants of today have been at a loss to know what to make of Cunninghame's accounts, as there are pages and pages of them still in existence. Business procedures were not then closely defined by a body of law as they are now. Legislation came in the wake of hundreds of cases like the Warner v Cunninghame case, in which business associates were unhappy with each other's performance. At that time no single method of book-keeping had won universal acceptance and, as individuals employed their own methods of accounting, examples of inconsistencies within a set of accounts are not difficult to find.

THE BEAUMONT ERA

Robert Reid Cunninghame died in 1814, a man much respected in Ayrshire for the contribution he had made to economic growth in the county. Before his death he had arranged that several members of his family should benefit from having a share in the colliery. The bulk of his estate went to his eldest surviving son, Robert, who was the second son from his second marriage (to Annabella Reid). Ann, Robert's sister, also benefited. But a share in the colliery also went to John, the son of Elizabeth, Robert Reid Cunninghame's daughter from his first marriage (to Elizabeth Hamilton) and to her husband Major George Vanburry Brown (Elizabeth died before her father). The arrangements were complicated, but the family was united in opposition to any suggestion that Patrick Warner should take on the management of the colliery.

Once again, recourse was made to the law, and the local sheriff appointed as manager Mr Beaumont, a man experienced in mining the coalfields around the Forth. His salary as colliery manager was set at £350 per annum. In the year after his appointment the profits of the Stevenston Coal Company fell from £2,000 to £400, a worrying situation for Beaumont, and a posthumous vindication, perhaps, of Robert Reid Cunninghame's management. The fall in profits cannot have been unrelated to a general fall in coal prices in Scotland after 1810, attributed by many in the coal industry to the increase in production at a time when demand was steady.[1] Price fixing cartels or combines developed in the Scottish coalfields as a result and coal masters actively discouraged the opening up of new pits.

Beaumont thought that a remedy for his particular problems lay in extracting coal from the Saltcoats-Campbell Lands (the area lying to the south of the present Saltcoats-Stevenston road, between the harbour and the Stevenston Burn) as there were reputedly large reserves of good quality workable coal there (as was proved recently during earth-moving work carried out in advance of the building of a new sewage pumping station).

Cunninghame immediately objected on the grounds that the coal under the Saltcoats-Campbell Lands belonged to him and was not part of the co-partnery agreement. It looked as if he had a good case. In a plan produced in 1798 Saltcoats-Campbell Lands are shown in white which indicates that they were not included in the original agreement made between Patrick Warner and Robert Reid Cunninghame. In the terms of that agreement, the co-partnery had the right to mine such coals in Saltcoats-Campbell as could be reached from shafts put down to extract coal from the lands included in the co-partnery's territory. With the mining technology available in the 1770s when the co-partnery was first formed, that would probably not have been a vast amount. The revised agreement of 1783 allowed shafts to be sunk in the Saltcoats-Campbell Lands between the Stevenston Burn and the Capon Craig Gaw. Even so, Robert Reid Cunninghame had probably thought of the Saltcoats-Campbell coal as a reserve to be exploited when all the coal on the co-partnery's land had been extracted.

His son certainly considered that it was his exclusively and more litigation followed. The case was heard at the Sheriff Court and the Sheriff found in favour of Beaumont. It was technically possible in the second decade of the 19th century to extract considerable quantities of coal from Saltcoats-Campbell using existing shafts. Forced ventilation allowed miners to work at far greater distances from the shafts than had been possible when the co-partnery was first formed. Underground roadways had been greatly improved and ponies were being used to transport coal from the face where it was worked to the shaft.

Although the Sheriff's decision gave Beaumont the authority to go ahead, Cunninghame continued to oppose him. He carried the case on to the House of Lords where, eventually, the Sheriff's decision was upheld.

Cunninghame countered by planning to sink new shafts in Saltcoats-Campbell and to mine there on his own account, independently of Beaumont and the Stevenston

Coal Company. In 1828 he bought a steam engine to work in a new shaft. Beaumont went to court to stop him. The legal judgement indicated that although the Saltcoats-Campbell land belonged exclusively to Cunninghame, the coal underneath was to be considered as belonging to the Stevenston Coal Company (the co-partnery) by virtue of the fact that it could be reached from existing shafts on land quite clearly within the Coal Company's territory.

Cunninghame had other difficulties to face. All was not well at the harbour. During his life-time, Robert Reid Cunninghame had acquired an interest in several boats that carried coal from Saltcoats to Ireland. A few, he owned outright. During busy periods at the harbour these boats were allowed to "jump the queue" and were able to load and unload ahead of boats that were independently owned. That practice created bad-feeling among boat owners and masters and they would have felt no particular loyalty to the owners of Saltcoats Harbour and, when harbour facilities became available at nearby Ardrossan, they were no doubt happy to use them instead. Moreover, Saltcoats Harbour was unsuitable for the bigger, deeper draught vessels that were then coming into service.

A further difficulty arose for Cunninghame over the matter of a rail link to Saltcoats Harbour. In 1826 the Ardrossan Canal Company whose original intention had been to build a canal from Glasgow to Ardrossan, having built the canal as far as Johnstone, decided that it would be better to link Johnstone and Ardrossan with a railway. The Company was prepared to run a branch line to Saltcoats Harbour and Cunninghame readily agreed. The railway line was to follow the route of the waggon way built by Robert Reid Cunninghame in 1812. An Act of Parliament was at that time required to allow major construction work such as harbours and railways to go ahead. When the Ardrossan Canal Company's proposal was debated, a member of the House of Lords pointed out that it would be illegal for the Company to construct a branch line on land it did not own. A final report on the business by the Court of Session dated 1853 stated that, though ownership of the land used as the route for the waggon way was contested in 1811, the then Earl of Eglinton had not pursued the case within the set time and thus the land was deemed to belong to Robert Reid Cunninghame. That being so, the route of the waggon way now belonged to his heir, and as Robert Cunninghame was not part of the Ardrossan Canal Company, the financing and maintenance of the proposed branch line would be his responsibility. The cost of raising the level of the existing waggon way to the level of the proposed railway and of extending the line right down to the pier was estimated at £3,000. Although the Ardrossan to Glasgow railway was completed in 1840, the waggon way, which had been improved, continued in use until 1852, when the harbour ceased to be used for the coal trade.

Robert Cunninghame died in 1858. His heir was his sister's son, Arthur Wellesley Robertson, who added Cunninghame to his name for the sake of continuity. Very little information is forthcoming from the Auchenharvie Papers concerning his activities. There is a reference to him agreeing to the lease of a dwelling house "at Canal bank near the magnesia works" to Kenneth and Whitefield Colliers in May 1863. After that - nothing. We can only presume that the Stevenston Coal Company (the co-partnery) continued till the end of its agreed term in 1869.

The reference to the lease is the last reference in the Auchenharvie Papers to the coal mining enterprise and the collection of papers ends soon after. The heirs of the

Cunninghame family ceased to have any direct involvement in the mining of coal, but it was very far from being the end of coal mining in the area. In fact it became even more important as new markets for coal opened up.

As the railways extended into virtually all parts of Scotland, the demand for coal to fuel the ever more powerful locomotives grew. At sea the increased use of, and dependence on, coal-burning marine steam engines stimulated demand. The Royal Navy established big coal reserves at "coaling ports", located in all parts of the Empire. Colliers regularly left Ardrossan Harbour carrying local coal for bunkering. Domestic coal consumption rose, partly because supplies of coal were by this time regular and dependable. There was a big demand for coking coal for use in the iron industry and iron foundries were established on and near coalfields to minimise the cost of transporting coal. The Auchenharvie coalfield was no exception and a firm of iron-founders from Edinburgh, Merry and Cunninghame (no relation to the Auchenharvie Cunninghames), established an iron-foundry there. It is possible that local iron ore was used initially and there was limestone available nearby as well (lime was an essential ingredient in the smelting process, chemically combining with non-ferrous compounds in the iron ore forming "basic slag" which could be run off in its molten state).

The Glengarnock Iron Company leased land and pits near Stevenston and William Baird & Co. also established an iron works. By the 1860s, the Auchenharvie-Ardeer-Saltcoats-Campbell estates had largely been transformed from agricultural holdings into an industrial area. The transformation was a lengthy process, starting with Robert Cunninghame's opening up of the coalfield in 1678, but it was thorough, and the effects were cumulative. The population increased as people moved into the area to work in the expanding industries. The pre-existing small villages of Stevenston and Saltcoats grew beyond all recognition as did the new, planned, town of Ardrossan, begun in 1820. As the population expanded, the demand for services grew, creating opportunities for builders, grocers, hauliers, milliners, drapers, tailors and, of course, lawyers. In addition, the vital coal trade with Ireland depended on there being a fleet of suitable vessels and there were opportunities in ship-building and repair.

The success of the mining industry itself created ancillary industries. To begin with these supporting industries would have been relatively simple - making baskets to carry coal in, or corves, the open wooden boxes that could be loaded with coal and dragged along the workings to the bottom of the shaft. Later, local blacksmiths were used to make some parts of the early steam pumping engines and as the pumping and winding engines grew more sophisticated and more numerous, a community of mill wrights and engineers evolved to construct and maintain them.

We can also see in the making of sea-salt, the beginnings of the local chemical industry. At first salt-making expanded in keeping with the coal mining. Sea-salt was expensive and contained a high proportion of impurities compared with the mined salt that could be obtained from the continent. But while that was difficult to obtain during the Napoleonic Wars, the local industry thrived. The imposition of the heavy Salt Tax was intended to protect the manufacturers of sea-salt in Britain from foreign imports, but the pressure of the growing demand for good quality salt led, in the end, to the free-er importation of continental salt and most Scottish saltworks went out of business.[2] The Saltcoats works hung on longer than many because home produced salt was generally thought to be better suited to the preparation of local butter, cheese and bacon, giving them a distinctive flavour. In fact there was heated debate about whether cheese made from local milk but seasoned with imported salt could truthfully be called "Dunlop Cheese". In the meantime, however, some of the impurities, such as magnesia and Epsom salts (magnesium sulphate) which were precipitated out of the sea water during the salt making process were found to be valuable in their own right and small works were established for their production.

[1] Duckham, B.F.: *A History of the Scottish Coal Industry, Vol.1*
[2] Whatley, C.A: *The Scottish Salt Industry 1570-1850*

LOOKING BACK

Looking back over the industrialisation of North Ayrshire we can see that Robert Cunninghame and Robert Reid Cunninghame played key roles in the process. However, their achievements were not unique. Other land owners and entrepreneurs were, of course, carrying out similar schemes in other parts of the Ayrshire coalfield, and indeed in other coalfields throughout Scotland, but both these members of the Cunninghame family seem to have been distinguished by their great enthusiasm and dedication. It is difficult, if not impossible, at this distance to ascertain what motivated them; clearly, they must have been sustained through their financial, legal and other difficulties by some sort of vision of an industrious and prosperous future. They certainly were not in the 'get rich quick' brigade.

With hindsight that vision can be viewed as a blinkered one. There is nothing in all the pages and pages of the Auchenharvie Papers to suggest that they had any inkling of the cost of coal extraction in terms of the human suffering and environmental damage that it could and did cause. Did they ever go underground to gain first-hand knowledge of the working conditions in their own pits? Did they not notice the bings of rock waste and debris accumulating in the countryside? If they did, they did not record their reactions.

The absence in the Auchenharvie Papers of any reference to the men, women and children who hewed the coal, brought it to the surface, sorted and cleaned it, is striking. We know far more about the machines than the miners. We know how many horses Robert Reid Cunninghame employed, but not how many people were in his work-force. We know about the minutiae of the legal wranglings but virtually nothing about the day to day operations of a single pit.

While it is no doubt true that some things are more likely to be committed to writing than others and that some pieces of writing are more likely to be thought worth keeping than others, it does seem strange that so little information about the running of the business at a practical level can be gleaned from the papers of a family that was so deeply involved.

There are random pages here and there showing amounts of money paid to named men, presumably miners who appear to have been the leaders of small work gangs. These pages do not tell us, though, how many were in the gangs; whether they were all hewers; whether they included bearers and other underground workers; whether the gangs were made up of women and children as well as men. Nor do they tell us what the payments represented and how they were divided up among the work-gang members. However, if the practice followed by the Cunninghames was the same as in other better documented collieries, the payments would have been made according to how many loads of coal each gang brought to the surface over a given period, not according to how many hours per day and days per week each individual member of the gang had worked during that period.

The one detailed reference to actual miners and salters is not one that resounds to the credit of the family. It concerns the case brought in 1760 against three men by John Reid, Robert Reid Cunninghame's father, when he was in charge of the business. He claimed that they were bound to the Stevenston Colliery and had absconded to work at another colliery in Ayrshire. They defended themselves by saying that John Reid had given them no work for such a long period that they and their families were destitute, so that they had been forced to look for work elsewhere. Nevertheless, they were ordered to return to Stevenston. The case occurred at a time when the serfdom status of miners was being phased out, when new men coming in to the industry to work had no legal restraints put upon their coming and going, but existing miners still had to make an application to their local sheriff to have their serfdom ended. John Reid was within his rights to have the two men sent back, but it seems a mean and vindictive act.

There is no way of knowing if this incident was characteristic of the family's dealings with the men and women who toiled in their mines. The almost total lack of any other evidence on the matter of worker-owner relationships does not suggest that the Cunninghames gave much thought to the subject at all. Not many colliery owners did. The results of their indifference to their worker's conditions became apparent in the 19th Century from the evidence collected by various Royal Commissions. Information about working conditions in local collieries during the second half of the 19th Century and about the miners' and others' strenuous attempts to force improvements, can be found in abundance in the Ardrossan and Saltcoats Herald as well as in other contemporary local and national newspapers. However, by that time the Cunninghames played no active part in the industry. Their day was over.

BIBLIOGRAPHY

Burns, J.W. (ed.)	*Miscellaneous Writings of John Spruell*
Craig, G.E. (ed.)	*The Geology of Scotland,* Oliver & Boyd, 1965
Duckham, B.F.	*A History of the Scottish Coal Industry, Vol.1,* David & Charles, 1970
Graham, E.J.	*The Shipping Trade of Ayrshire 1689-1791,* Ayrshire Archaeological & Natural History Society, 1991
Hume, J.R.	*The Industrial Archaeology of Scotland, Vol.1: The Lowlands and Borders,* Batsford, 1976
Levy, Catriona	*Ardrossan Harbour,* W.E.A., 1988
Pont, Timothy	*Cunninghame Topographised 1604-1608,* 1876
Robertson, G.	*A Genealogical account of the Principal Families in Ayrshire, Vol.1,* Irvine, 1823
Robertson, G.	*Rural Recollections,* Irvine, 1829
Scott, N.M.	"Documents relating to coal mining in the Saltcoats district in the first quarter of the 18thCentury", *Scottish Historical Review Vol. 19,* 1922
Sinclair, Sir John (ed.)	*The Statistical Account of Scotland* (Old Statistical Account), 1791-99
Whatley, C.A.	*The Finest Place for a Lasting Colliery,* Ayrshire Archaeological & Natural History Society, 1983
Whatley, C.A.	*The Scottish Salt Industry 1570-1850,* Aberdeen University Press, 1987
Other references	*The Statistical Account of Scotland* (New Statistical Account), Wm. Blackwood & Sons, 1845

❖